S0-BCX-818

This Book Belongs To:

_____

Values To Live By™ Classic Stories

Alice in Wonderland

Black Beauty

Call of the Wild

The Jungle Book

Pinocchio

Robinson Crusoe

Secret Garden

Swiss Family Robinson

Treasure Island

20,000 Leagues Under the Sea

Wonderful Wizard of Oz

VALUES TO LIVE BY™

www.valuestoliveby.com

ISBN 1-933443-17-0
ISBN 978-1-933443-17-1

FREDERIC THOMAS INC.
Produced by: Frederic Thomas Inc., Naples, Florida, Tel: 239-593-8000.

A Classic Story About Patience

Robinson Crusoe

By Daniel Defoe
Retold by Lisl H. Detlefsen
Illustrated by José Miralles

Managing Art Editor Tom Gawle
Senior Editor Mary Weber
Designer Tim Carls

FREDERIC THOMAS INC.

Robinson Crusoe

The inspiration for Daniel Defoe's *Robinson Crusoe* came from the true story of William Selkirk, who was stranded on an island in the Pacific Ocean. Due to the fame of Selkirk's adventure and Defoe's novel, this island is now known as Robinson Crusoe Island. It is one of three islands in the Juan Fernández archipelago, or island group. These islands are part of Chile and are located about 400 miles off the coast of South America. While Selkirk lived alone, Robinson Crusoe Island is now home to about 500 people.

Just like the beautiful wildlife described in Defoe's story adventures, the real island is home to dozens of native plant species that cannot be found anywhere else in the world.

While Selkirk was only on his island for a

few years, Crusoe stays on his fictional island for 28 years, 2 months and 19 days. During this time, Crusoe discovers how important patience can be when learning to live alone in a new place. Eventually, Crusoe begins to accept his situation and finds happiness in his new life. Toward the end of his time on the island, he also finds a friend who he rescues and calls "Friday." *Robinson Crusoe* has been and continues to be the inspiration for many other adventure stories.

Daniel Defoe (1660-1731) was born in London, the third child of James and Mary Foe. While his father wanted him to become a minister, Defoe had other ideas. Before becoming a novelist, Defoe worked as a traveling salesman, a merchant, a political journalist and a spy. He published his first novel, *Robinson Crusoe*, in 1719. The simple and fact-based style of his writing became very popular in English novels. Defoe wrote many other books, including sequels to *Robinson Crusoe* and a three-volume guidebook, *A Tour Through the Whole Island of Great Britain*.

VALUABLE FOOTSTEPS

Stories like *Robinson Crusoe* are fun to read and think about, but can also teach us about the world and ourselves. *Robinson Crusoe* is a great story to teach us about the word *patience*. Being patient means that you keep trying, even if something is difficult or takes a long time to do. You can learn more about the value *patience* by trying to understand what Robinson Crusoe is thinking or feeling and how he views the world.

Try the following little activity with a parent, sister, brother or friend while you read the story. First, watch for footsteps within the book pages. They will lead you to a special paragraph where you can pretend to be Robinson Crusoe. By "walking in his shoes," you can begin to understand him. Then talk about how you would feel and what you would do if you took his place. Would you keep trying, or would you give up? What could you do to better help yourself? What would you do to make the island your home?

❦ Adventures at Sea ❦

SEPTEMBER 30, 1659. I, poor miserable Robinson Crusoe, being shipwrecked during a dreadful storm, came on shore of this dismal, secluded island, all the rest of the ship's crew being drowned and myself almost dead.

It is in this way that I began to keep my journal. To tell the tale of how I came to be shipwrecked, I must go back to the beginning. I was born in the year 1632 in England. By the time I was a young man, I was determined to go to sea despite my father's warnings against it. On my first voyage, a terrible storm caused our ship to sink just moments after our rescue. Ashamed to go home, I instead boarded a vessel bound to Africa. This was to be my only successful voyage.

On my next voyage, a Turkish rover from Sallee attacked our ship as we were making our course around the Canary Islands. We were all carried into the Sallee port as prisoners, and the captain of the rover made me his captive servant. I dreamed of escaping, but it wasn't until two years had passed that an odd circumstance presented itself. It was when the captain ordered me to go out in his boat to catch some fish that I made my escape. I did not stop or go on shore until I had sailed for five days. Eventually, I saw a Portuguese ship and fired a gun as a signal of distress. The captain saw my signal and kindly took me on board.

We arrived safely in All Saints' Bay in the Brazils. I went on shore and had not been there long when I resolved to purchase land and form a plantation. After four years, I began to live and succeed very well on my land. Despite my new wealth, I could not resist an offer made by some fellow planters. They proposed that I sail to the coast of Guinea to conduct our trading at that port. In exchange, they agreed to look after my plantation in my absence.

I left for Africa on September 1, 1659, exactly eight years after I left my family to go to sea. Our ship was large and carried 14 men besides the master, his boy and myself. After almost two weeks of very good weather, a violent hurricane blew in such a terrible way for 12 days, that every day I expected to be swallowed up by the sea. As we could no longer make our voyage to Africa without some assistance, the captain resolved to change our course and steer northwest by west in order to reach some of our English islands. Soon after, a second storm drove us off our course again. We had no sooner seen land when the wind blew very hard and pushed the ship onto a sandbank. Solidly stuck upon the bank, the ship received repeated pounding from the fierce sea. We knew nothing about where we were nor if we could release her from the sand. The rage of the wind was still so great that we could not hope to have the ship hold much longer. Gripped with fear, we took a boat from on board the ship and slung it over the ship's side. Desperately, 11 of us climbed into it, committing ourselves to the wild sea.

Our situation was very dismal, indeed. We all saw plainly, the sea being so high, the boat could not survive. After we had rowed

quite a distance, a raging wave overset the boat, separating us. Though I swam very well, I could not come out of the waves to draw breath until a wave carried me toward the shore, leaving me upon the land. I got to my feet and ran as fast as I could, but soon another wave as high as a great hill came over me. I could feel the mighty force of the wave as it carried me away from the shore. I held my breath and tried to assist myself by swimming forward with all my might. Over and over, I fought against the waves. Once a wave pushed me up against a rock with such force that it beat the breath out of my body. I was able to recover by holding on to the rock, and I resolved to hold fast. Then I climbed down and ran so far that the next wave could not carry me away. I ran to the mainland and clambered up the cliffs of the shore. There I collapsed on the grass, quite out of reach of the water.

Finding no sign of my fellow shipmates alive, I knew that I alone had landed safely on shore. I thanked God that my life was saved. I looked around to see what kind of place I was in and discovered my misfortunate circumstances. I was wet, had no other clothes than those I was wearing and had nothing to eat or drink. It seemed likely to me that I would die of hunger or be eaten by wild beasts. This was particularly upsetting as I had no weapon either to hunt for my food or defend myself against any creature that might want me for theirs. As I was extremely tired, I climbed a tree and fell fast asleep. ❧

❊ Sole Survivor ❊

When I awoke the next day, the storm had passed. In the night, the ship had been pushed from the sandbar up onto some rocks. I thought that if I could get on board, I might save some things for my use. So I swam up to the ship and pulled myself into it with the help of a rope that hung down from inside. The ship had a great deal of water in it, but it lay such that most of the provisions were dry. I found three wooden beams and tied them together to form a raft. To make it stronger, I added three lengths of a spare topmast that I had cut with the carpenter's saw.

Then I lowered the provisions into the raft, including three seaman's chests that I emptied and filled with bread, rice, cheese and grain. After some searching, I found the carpenter's chest, the tools in which being very valuable to me. I next took some ammunition and arms, some powder horns, a small bag of bullets and two rusty swords. After my raft was full, I paddled back to the island using some broken oars I found in the ship. At length, I saw a cove on the shore into which I guided my raft. I fastened it by sticking my two broken oars into the ground, one on either side.

Next it was my job to seek a proper place to live and store my goods. I traveled to the top of a hill and discovered that I was on an island. There was no other land to be seen, except for some rocks that were a great way off and two small islands to the west. The island I was on seemed uninhabited except by animals, of which I saw only birds. Content with my knowledge, I went back to my raft and went to work to bring my cargo ashore. I considered that many other things on the ship might be useful, so I got back on board the ship. I loaded the raft with some nails and more tools, a perspective glass, all the clothes I could find, a spare sail, a hammock and some bedding. Once on shore, I made a little tent out of the sail and some poles and put into it everything that I knew would spoil either with rain or sun. Then I blocked the door of the tent with some boards and went to sleep.

Every day I returned to the ship, each time taking more goods that could prove useful. I had to be patient not to overload my raft. On my 12th trip, I took some gold and silver coins, even though I had no use for them on the island. That night, a storm destroyed what was left of the ship, but there was little left in it that was of use to me.

I soon discovered that I needed a place to live. I found a little plain on the side of a rising hill. The hill had a hollow spot that was worn away at the side. I pitched my tent on the flat land next to the hollow spot. Around the tent and hollow I made a strong fence with cable and two rows of strong stakes that were about five-and-a-half feet tall and sharpened at the top. This was very hard work and took a long time to finish. I made a ladder to climb in and out of my fort and carried all of my provisions and goods into it for safe-keeping.

After this, I worked my way into the rock, making a cave just behind my tent for a cellar. I patiently worked for days until these things were brought to perfection.

I went out at least once every day with my gun to see if I could pursue anything fit for food. I discovered that there were goats on the island, which I learned to hunt after some difficulty. To prevent myself from losing track of time, I made a great cross with a large post and used my knife to carve a notch for every day, making every seventh notch longer and every first day of the month longer still. Thus I kept my calendar, or weekly, monthly and yearly recording of time.

All of my work took a great deal of time and effort because of my limited tools. For example, if I wanted a board I had to cut down a tree, place it on its edge and make both sides flat with my ax. While by this method I could only make one board out of a whole tree, I had no solution to this except patience. When I had made enough of these boards, I made large shelves in my cave so that I could separate my goods. I also made a table and a chair. Now I could sit and write in my journal with the ink and paper I had taken from the ship. I began by writing what had happened to me since the shipwreck, starting on September 30th. I kept the journal until I was forced to stop when I ran out of ink. ❧

❧ The Journal ❧

NOVEMBER 4. **This morning I began** to order my times of work, hunting, sleeping, etc. Every morning, if it did not rain, I walked out with my gun for two hours, then worked until about eleven. Then I ate and napped from twelve to two. In the evening I worked again. Every time my hunting was successful, I took off the skins and saved them.

DECEMBER 27. While hunting, I captured a young goat. I led the goat home and bound its injured leg. I took such care of it that it grew tame and would not go away. I thought that I might be able to breed some tame goats for food when my ammunition is gone.

JANUARY 30. Being in great need of a candle, I saved the fat from the goat meat and put it in a dish made of clay. I added a wick made out of a plant and made myself a lamp.

MARCH 6. After some heavy rains, I found about 12 ears of barley growing in the spot where I had shaken out a bag of chicken feed months before. I hoped to replant the grain so that in time I would have enough to make bread.

JUNE 17. I found a large turtle at the seaside that had 60 eggs inside of her. I cooked and ate the meat. It was to me the most flavorful and pleasant meal that I had ever tasted, having had no meat but goats and birds since I landed in this horrible place.

JUNE 27. I have been terribly ill. My fever was so violent that I stayed in bed all day without eating or drinking. I slept all the next day and night.

JULY 3. The fever has left for good, though I have not yet recovered my full strength.

JULY 15. Now that my health is restored, I began to explore more of the island. On the bank of a brook I found many meadows covered with grass and other plants that I had not seen before.

JULY 16. After going some distance farther around the island, the country became more woody than before. In this part I found melons and grapes, very ripe and rich. I took the grapes with me to dry them in the sun and keep them as raisins. Everything was so fresh and green that it looked like a planted garden. I also saw many cocoa, orange, lemon and lime trees.

JULY 27. I became so enamored with this place that I built myself another home here and surrounded it with a double hedge of bushes as high as I could reach. Now I had my country house and my seacoast house.

SEPTEMBER 30. Having made 365 notches on my post, I found I had reached the unhappy anniversary of my landing upon this island. I prayed and did not eat until after the sun had gone down. Having been on the island for a year, I had seen the passing of rainy and dry seasons. I made a list to help me with my planting of crops. ❧

❊ Of Pots and Canoes ❊

By the time of my second anniversary of landing on the island, I concluded that it was possible for me to be happier in this solitary life than I might have imagined. I gave humble and hearty thanks to God for saving my life. I spent my time hunting or viewing the island as I traveled between my two houses. With so much to do, the days passed quickly.

I was seldom idle in my third year here. Every day I hunted for food and made things to improve my home. There were a great many things that I wanted, but had no way to furnish myself with but by hard labor and much experimenting. Remembering how the basket makers in England made their wickerware, I decided to try my hand at it. For the materials, I went to my country house and cut down a large quantity of twigs. I used them to make a great many woven baskets to carry things. They were not very handsome but certainly served their purpose.

I also wanted to make myself some containers out of clay. My first attempts were ugly and misshapen. Many of them fell in, fell out, cracked in the sun or fell to pieces.

It took me two months of hard labor to make two large, ugly earthen containers. Eventually I made several smaller things, such as little pots, dishes and pitchers with greater success. I would bake them in the heat of the sun until they were strong enough for use. I also learned to glaze the pots by placing them in the fire with firewood all round them and a great heap of embers under them. The sand that was mixed in with the clay would eventually melt and form a hard glaze around the pots. No joy was equal to mine as when I finally had pots to boil water and meat.

My next concern was to find a way to make bread. After several seasons of planting grain, I finally had enough to use. I hollowed a great block of hard wood using my ax and hatchet. Then I used another piece of hardwood to make a heavy beater. Together, these tools allowed me to grind the grain. Next I needed a sieve to separate the grain into the bran and the husk. I remembered I had stored some pieces of muslin in one of the seaman's chests. I made three small sieves out of this cloth. While I did not concern myself with the yeast, I certainly needed an oven. I made some earthen vessels about two feet wide and nine inches deep and glazed them in the fire. From then on, when I wanted bread, I made my loaves and baked them in these pans by putting the pans in the fire and covering them with embers. Everything took a long time to make because of my lack of tools, help and skill. It was hard work and patience that carried me through this task and many others. It need not be a surprise that all of these tasks took up most of my third year on the island.

All the while I was doing these things, I often wondered if there might be a way to leave the island. Thinking it might be possible to make myself a canoe, I went to work. It took me 20 days to hack down a cedar tree that was five foot ten inches in diameter and 22 feet tall. It took another month to shape it into something like the bottom of a boat and another three months to clear the inside.

When I had finished, it was big enough to carry 26 people along with me. After a lot of work attempting to get the canoe into the water without success, I gave up. Having again reached the passing of another year, I realized the error in beginning work before judging my own strength.

I had now been here so long that many of the things I had brought on shore were either gone or wasted. My clothes had begun to decay. Using the animal skins that I had saved and dried, I set about to make myself some new ones. First I made a goatskin cap to keep off the rain and sun. This went so well that I made myself an entire suit of clothes out of goatskin, including pants, a vest and an umbrella. I hung a little saw and a hatchet from a goatskin belt. I must admit that they were horribly made, for if I was a bad carpenter, I was a worse tailor. But they kept me cool in the sun and dry in the rain.

Another five years passed without any extraordinary events. I lived on in the same way, planting my grain, drying raisins and hunting. I also made a smaller, more practical canoe. While this canoe was much too small to be much help in an attempt to leave, I decided to use it to make a tour around the island. The journey took a dangerous turn when I became caught in a current. It carried my boat farther and farther away. How miserable a creature I was! I looked back at my desolate island as the most pleasant place in the world

and wished more than anything to be there again. I scolded myself for being so ungrateful of my good situation on the island. After some time, I felt a breeze on my face. I spread my sail and used the force of the breeze to get out of the current. While I was glad to return to the island, I was now on the opposite side from the one I started from. I reached my country house by the next evening and stayed there to sleep.

After my voyage, I decided I had now had enough of adventure at sea. I accepted my life on the island and decided that I lived very happily in all things except company. I spent my time making improvements on my pottery, baskets and homes. By my 11th year in residence on the island, my ammunition was low. It was time to see if I could trap any additional goats. I dug several large pits in the earth in places where I had seen the goats eating. After several disappointments, I caught three kids, a male and two females. I was able to tame the goats, and I built a fence to keep them in. A year and a half later, I had a flock of 12 goats. In two years more I had 43. Not only did I have a fresh supply of meat, but milk, too. I also learned how to make butter and cheese after many experiments. I lived on in this happy manner in want of nothing but human companionship.

❧ A Footprint, Fear and the Lost Ship ❧

One day in my 15th year on the island, I saw a man's footprint in the sand near the shore! I stood there completely stunned, unable to imagine how it got there. Then I went up and down the shore, searching for another footprint, but I could not see anything. I measured the footprint against my own and found my foot to be much smaller! I went home alarmed, looking behind me every few steps and mistaking every bush and tree to be a man. After that, I had many wild ideas of being attacked. In fear, I made another wall around my fort by planting young trees and reinforcing them with timber and old cables. I made seven little holes in the wall and planted a musket into each one so that I could fire them all in a few minutes time. In six years, the trees had grown into a wall so thick and strong that no man could break into it or even imagine that anything was beyond it. Despite my work, I felt uneasy.

When wandering further west on the island than I had ever done before, I came upon another unsettling discovery. To my horror, I saw the shore spread with skulls and other human bones. I also observed a place where a fire had been made and a circle dug in the earth. I ran to my seacoast house with all the speed I could. After this, I was more fearful than ever. I kept close to my home for years, leaving only to tend to the grain or my goats.

Early one December morning during my 23rd year on the island, I was surprised to see the light of a fire upon the shore about two miles away. I climbed to the side of a hill where there was a flat place and looked in the direction of the light.

I saw nine native islanders sitting around a fire. Their canoes were resting on the shore. Even after they left, their presence worried me greatly. I spent most of my time in a horrible mood, thinking about what I should do the next time I saw them.

I had a surprise of another kind the following May. On this day, there was a very great storm with a great deal of thunder and lightning. I was reading my Bible when I heard a gun fired at sea. I thought it must be a ship in trouble. While I could not help them, I thought that they might help me. So, I brought together all the dry wood that I had and went up to the top of the hill and set a fire. I kept the fire going all night long. When the morning came and the storm cleared up, I could see something out at sea. I ran down to the south side of the island. By this time, the weather was perfectly clear. To my great sorrow, I could plainly see the wreck of a ship cast away in the night upon some concealed rocks. I decided to venture out in my boat to this wreck, thinking I might find something on board that might be useful to me.

I prepared for the voyage by taking some bread, a pot of water and some raisins down to my boat. After paddling for two hours I came up to it. It was a sad sight. The ship, which by its building was Spanish, was stuck fast between two rocks. I went on board and found that there were no survivors. Most of the goods had been spoiled by the water, but I did take a powder horn, a fire shovel and tongs, two little brass kettles, a copper pot and two seaman's chests. When I opened the chests back at home, I found several things of great use to me such as shirts and handkerchiefs. I also found three bags of coins and almost a pound of gold bars. As I had no use for the money on the island, I would have given it all for stockings and shoes. ❧

❧ Adventures with Friday ❧

Some time passed before anything else disrupted my quiet life on the island. Early one morning, I was surprised to see five canoes on the shore, the people who belonged to them all out of my sight. I climbed up to the top of the hill as I did before and saw 30 native islanders. I also saw two miserable captives, also natives, one of whom was standing by himself. In that very moment, the poor prisoner saw that none of the others were watching him. With incredible speed, he ran along the sand toward my home on the coast. To my relief, only two men followed him. It then occurred to me that this was my chance to save his life and perhaps gain a companion. I ran down the hill, fetched my two guns and ran toward the natives following their prisoner. I knocked one of them down with my gun. The other took up his bow and arrow to shoot at me, so I was forced to shoot him first. The poor prisoner stopped running when he saw both of his enemies had fallen, but he was afraid of my gun. I motioned to him to come to me. He finally came close, kneeled down and kissed the ground to show his gratitude for my help. Though I could not understand him when he spoke, his words sounded wonderful to me. His was the first human voice that I had heard for about 25 years.

Before returning to my home, we went to the top of the hill and I saw through my perspective glass that the other natives had left in their canoes, taking with them the two I fought off. Now that I had the opportunity to observe my new companion, I saw that he was a handsome man with strong limbs, about 26 years old. His hair was long and black and his skin was a very tawny, agreeable color. His face was round with a small nose. After he had rested for some time, I began to speak to him and teach him to speak to me. First, I taught him his name Friday, a name I gave him based on the day I saved his life. I then taught him to say yes and no and to understand their meanings. I gave Friday a pair of linen pants that I found in the Spanish ship and made him a goatskin jacket. I also gave him a hareskin cap. These clothes felt awkward to Friday at first, but eventually he liked them very well. While I was initially cautious in my interactions with Friday, I soon learned that there never was a man who had a more faithful, caring, sincere friend than Friday was to me. I made it my business to teach him everything I could to make him helpful. He was a happy and hard-working student and learned quickly. I taught him to speak English and to be a good Christian. I was very pleased with his company.

The year that passed was the happiest year of all my life on the island. With two mouths to feed, I planted more wheat than before. Friday helped in all tasks and worked very willingly and very hard. We talked a great deal to each other. I asked Friday a thousand questions about his home, his people, the sea, the coast and what nations were near. He told me that west of his country there lived some white-bearded men, which I understood to mean the Spaniards who had survived the shipwreck. I asked if we could leave the island and find these men. Friday answered that this was possible in a large boat the size of two canoes. After this, I began to hope that I might find an opportunity to escape the island with Friday's help.

After some time, I asked Friday if he was willing to return to his own nation. When he expressed a desire to go home, I showed him the little canoe. Friday thought that this boat was too small to go so far. Then I showed him my first boat that I had made. While this boat was big enough, it had been laying in the sun for over 20 years and had split and become rotten. Friday and I went to work to build a large canoe to make our voyage. We found a proper tree and after a month's hard labor, we finished our boat. It took us another two weeks to get the boat into the water, but once it was in, it would have carried 20 people with ease. ❧

❊ Strangers Return ❊

I was now beginning my 27th year on the island, the last three of which I spent with Friday. With our new boat near completion, I thought that I would not be here another year. However, I went on with my work as before. By the time we finished making the mast and sails, it was the rainy season. Friday built a little dock to keep the rain off of the boat. We decided to wait for December to make our adventure.

When the good weather returned, we prepared for our trip daily. One morning, I called to Friday to ask him to find a turtle for our meal. He had not been gone long when he returned, crying out, "O yonder there! Three canoe!" The natives that had taken Friday prisoner had returned to the island. I told Friday that we must fight them. We went up the side of the hill and saw 21 natives, 2 prisoners and 3 canoes. They had landed near a thick wood near the sea. We marched down to the wood and saw the natives sitting around a fire. Friday and I took our aim with two muskets and fired at the same time. We continued to shoot until all the natives had fled in fear.

Then we ran over to the prisoner that was tied up on the shore. While Friday continued to fire at the

natives who were trying to escape in their canoes, I untied the poor victim. When he had recovered some strength, he told me that he was Spanish.

By the time the battle had ended, only four natives had escaped in one of their canoes. Friday and I intended to follow them, but when we reached another canoe we were surprised to find the other prisoner lying in it, bound tightly. When Friday saw him, he cried and hugged the man. It was a good while before Friday was able to explain his behavior. When he calmed down he explained that this was his father! We brought the Spaniard and Friday's father back to my home on the coast so that they could rest in comfort.

After the two rescued prisoners had been fed and given shelter and time to rest, we began a conversation. Because of my concern about the natives who had escaped, I told Friday to ask his father if he thought they might return. He answered that they were so frightened by the attack and the noise and fire of the guns that they would never return.

The Spaniard informed us that there were 16 more of his countrymen living at peace with Friday's people, but that they did not have enough food. I found out that I was correct in guessing that these men were the survivors of the shipwreck that I had witnessed. This gave me a new idea. I thought that if we could go to Friday's country and return to the island with the Spanish men, we might be able to build a boat large enough to carry us all away to the Brazils in the south or the islands in the north. The Spaniard told me that he believed that his men would agree to this plan. As it was, they were at the mercy of the natives because they had neither weapons nor food and had lost all hope of returning home.

While my first thought was to send Friday's father and the Spaniard to bring back the rest of the shipwrecked men, the Spaniard convinced me to wait. He had been with us a month and helped with the growing of grain and drying of grapes. He pointed out that the food we currently had would not be enough for the four of us along with 16 others. He suggested that we wait for another harvest, giving us time to plant and store enough food for his countrymen's arrival. I decided to follow this advice. After all, I had patiently waited this long and could wait a little longer still.

So we went to work. We sowed more grain and tried to increase the flock of tame goats as much as possible. We also cut and dried grapes in the sun. Before long, we had enough food for all 16 Spaniards and the four of us to last long enough to sail to any part of the world. In October, Friday's father and the Spaniard left in one of the native's canoes. I gave them enough food for the journey there and back and wished them a good voyage. I was quite excited to put our plan into action, for I had now been on the island for 28 years and some days. ❧

❧ The Mutineers ❧

Friday and I waited for their return for eight days. One morning, Friday came running to me and called out that they had returned. I jumped up and ran toward the sea. I saw a boat, but it was not the one we were expecting. I climbed the hill to get a better look and saw that it was an English longboat that appeared to be coming from an English ship at anchor in the sea. I knew that if this boat were really English, they must be up to no good in this part of the world. I saw 11 men come on shore, three of them tied up. As Friday and I watched, we knew that we must save these prisoners.

We waited until the sailors made their way into the woods to rest. The three prisoners sat under a tree, too upset to sleep. I decided to show myself to them and learn what had happened. When I approached the tree, they looked frightened.

"Do not be surprised," I said. "Perhaps you have a friend near you when you did not expect it."

"He must be sent from Heaven then," said one of them in a solemn voice, "for our condition is past the help of man."

"Lay aside your fears. I am an Englishman who wants to help you. I only have one companion, but we have arms and ammunition," I answered.

The prisoner explained that he was captain of the ship, but his men fought against him and took over. They landed on the island to leave the captain, his mate and a passenger there to die. I told him that I would help recover his ship if he would agree to two conditions. The first was that he would listen to me and do what I asked of him.

As to the second request, I asked him to take Friday and myself back to England on his ship. After the captain agreed to these conditions, I gave each man a musket and we made our plan.

We stormed into the woods where the other men were sleeping. Two of them woke up and made some noise, but it was too late. The moment they cried out, the captain's mate and the passenger captured the two. We surrounded the rest. The captain told the mutineers that he would spare their lives if they were sorry for their betrayal and promised to help take back the ship. The men all swore their loyalty to the captain, and he was willing to believe them. Even so, we bound their hands and feet to prevent another revolt.

Now our job was to recover the ship, which still had 26 men on board who had been part of the takeover. While we were planning what to do, we heard the ship fire a gun as a signal to call the other boat back. When the boat did not return, the ship sent another boat to shore with 10 armed men. Once on shore, the men gave three great shouts for their companions; but as they were now under our orders, they made no response. Then the new arrivals headed toward the woods to look for the others. I advanced my whole army, which was now made up of myself, Friday, the captain and his two men, and three prisoners that he trusted with weapons. We came upon them in the dark and were able to overtake them. The captain told the men to lay down their arms and give up their boat, which they did while begging for their lives.

The captain chose the prisoners he most trusted to go with him in the two longboats to surprise the ship. Friday and I stayed on the island to watch the others. Once the captain and his men were on board the ship, they caught the new rebel captain and gained control without losing any more lives. Once the ship was secured, the captain ordered seven guns to be fired as a signal of their success. Having heard the signal, a wave of relief and weakness came over me and I fell asleep. ✿

❦ Return to England and to the Island ❧

The next sound I heard was that of the captain telling me that the ship was all mine. I was ready to faint with surprise, and I broke into tears. I could hardly believe that after patiently living on the island for 28 years, 2 months and 19 days, I would, at last, return home.

The captain brought me some clothes from the ship, complete with gloves, shoes and stockings. After years of wearing loose goatskin clothing, such fine clothing felt quite unpleasant. The captain allowed several of the mutineers to stay on the island rather than sail to England as prisoners. When they declared their willingness to stay, I showed them how to plant grain, make bread, dry grapes, manage the goats and do all that was necessary to live there. I also told them the story of the Spaniards who were expected to return to the island and made them promise to treat them with kindness.

As for Friday, he agreed to go with me to England. When the ship was ready to sail, I carried on board my goatskin cap and the money that I had saved from both shipwrecks, which had been useless for so long.

After a long voyage, I arrived in England on June 11, 1687, having been away for almost 36 years. Being gone for so long made me feel like a stranger who had never been there. I learned that both my parents had died. I also discovered that despite my long absence, my partners in the Brazils had managed my plantation very well. Not wishing to settle in the Brazils, I sold the plantation to my loyal partners.

I thought more and more about returning to the island, so I boarded a ship in 1694 and visited there. I heard the stories of the Spaniards and how they did not get along with the Englishmen at first. Five of them managed to go to the mainland and brought back 11 men and 5 women. Because of this, there were about 20 young children now on the island. I stayed for about 20 days and left some tools, clothes and ammunition. Maybe someday I will write more about all of these things, including some very surprising incidents that occurred in some of my new adventures. ❧

What do you think?

Reading a book is like taking a magic carpet ride into a new and different world. In the world of Robinson Crusoe, you experienced exciting adventures right along with him! Classic stories like this one are fun to read, but also teach us about the world and ourselves. Wouldn't it be fun to share what you've learned with a brother, sister, friend or parent? Find a quiet spot to talk; then use the questions on the next two pages to discuss *Robinson Crusoe* and the valuable lessons it teaches.

1. Being *patient* means that you keep trying, even if something is difficult or takes a long time to do. What are some things that Robinson Crusoe did on the island that required patience?

_____

_____

_____

_____

_____

2. Sometimes it is hard to be patient when we are learning how to do something. Why is it important to be patient when learning a new skill?

_____

_____

_____

_____

_____

3. Would Robinson Crusoe's life on the island have been different if he had not been a patient person? If so, how?

_____

_____

_____

_____

_____

4. What were some of the things Robinson Crusoe did in an attempt to leave the island? How did patience play a role in his escape efforts?

_____

_____

_____

_____

_____